Deep in the rain forest, the air is hot and sticky. It smells like wet leaves. Plants grow as tall as skyscrapers. Their dark shadows hide many animals. But one tiny creature isn't hidden at all.

1

It's a poison dart frog. She's as small as a nickel. Her skin is bright red and blue with black polka dots. There she goes! She hops across the forest floor and scoots under a leaf to lay her eggs.

A coati sniffs the eggs, but doesn't eat them. Why? The coati is hunting for its favorite food — crunchy spiders!

One-two-three-four-five! Five slimy tadpoles hatch from the eggs. But they can't stay on this leaf for long. They need to live in water. Mother frog must find them a wet home NOW!

The first tadpole wriggles onto her back for a ride. Sticky ooze on the mother's skin glues the baby in place. Then off the frog hops to find her baby a home. There's room for only one tadpole on this trip.

How about the river? Whoosh! The deep water rushes by. No. This would not be a good home. The river would wash her tadpole away!

Plip-plop! Raindrops slap the leaves. Water! Just what her baby needs. Mother frog looks up a tree. It's covered with spiky plants. Each plant is like a cup, filling up with water.

Would this be a good home? There's plenty of water here. Clickety-clack! A crab darts out, snapping her claws as if to say, "Stay away! This is my home!"

Up and up, higher and higher, the little frog climbs. She's tired, but she can't stop now. She must find a home for her baby.

From its tree branch, a young harpy eagle eyes the frog. Mmm! Supper. That red skin looks so tasty! The bird swoops down and snatches the frog in its sharp beak.

But just as fast, the eagle spits it out.
That bright red skin has poison in it.
And it tastes TERRIBLE!

Mother frog and her baby land —
kerplop — on a branch. But they can't
stay here. They need to find a tadpole
home, FAST!

Mother frog scurries back up the tree. A family of termites jumps out of her path. Hip-hop. She scoots around a sleepy sloth. Then she spots it: a plant pool way up in the treetops. Maybe this will be a good home.

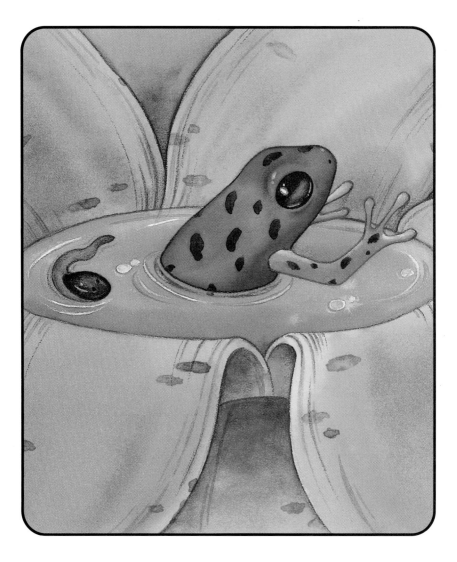

Yes, this is the perfect place! Mother
frog dips her back into the water. The
tiny tadpole slides off and swims
around, safe at last.

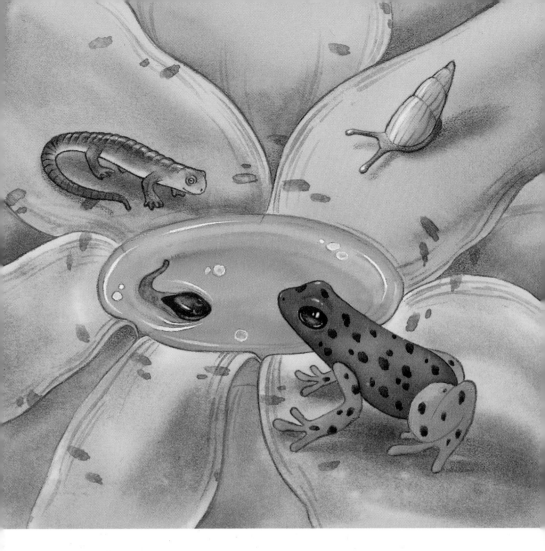

But now there's no time to lose. Far below, on the forest floor, four more tiny tadpoles are waiting. One by one, mother frog will find each a perfect home of its very own.